Dreary & Naughty

John LaFleur
&
Shawn Dubin

Requests for permission should be mailed to:
Permissions request, Dragonfly Productions LLC,
9 Appleton Street Suite 400 Boston, MA 02116

Library of Congress Cataloging-in-Publication Data available.

ISBN 0-9740838-1-X

First Edition

Published by:
Dragonfly Productions LLC 109 Fourth Ave Haddon Heights, NJ 08035
www.dragonflyprod.us
Dragonfly logo TM and © Dragonfly Productions LLC. All rights reserved.
Acetylene Comics 9 Appleton Street Suite 400 Boston, MA 02116
Acetylene Comics logo TM and © John LaFleur and Tyson Schroeder.
All rights reserved.

Design by Gino Verna.

Printed in Canada.

For The Believers: Gino, Pat, Tom, Shawn, and Trish
— John

For Mom and everyone that made this possible
— Shawn

Dreary and Naughty weren't two of a kind
Two more opposite friends, one could never find

Dreary was bony and chalky and grim
Naughty was pretty and sassy and slim

The two friends attended a regular school
Where Naughty left all the boys dripping with drool

The girls they found Dreary a bit of a ghoul
He accidentally scared them all into the pool

Naughty intimidated the girl's self-esteem
To look just like her, they could only dream

Her bangles bore inscriptions
Of words clever woven
Her boots covered feet
Of hooves that were cloven

Her smile was quite brilliant
Her teeth were bright white
The boys always tried
To keep her in sight

She was a bit different
With her long pointed tail
But it looked good on her
She was thin as a rail

Dreary just brought
All the boys down
When he'd come by
They would simply frown

He tried to dress like them
And bought all their clothes
But he preferred ones
Where the bones always showed

When it came to fashion
And trying to look cool
He had just one idiom
He said that "skulls rule"

So sometimes he passed
As a very cool kid
More often than not though
That's not what he did

School was a drag
It never went well
Both of them saw it
A small slice of hell

They'd often share classes
But sometimes they'd not
On those lonely days
They'd catch up at their spot

Everyday they hooked up
To partake in a lunch
And joke about mystery meat
That sometimes went "crunch"

All through their classes
Around the hall's bend
They stuck by each other
Until the day's end

Most of the kids
Would just point and stare
Neither of them seemed
To notice or care

The pair had each other
And thankfully so
For else they'd be lonely
Where ever they'd go

On the way home
Together they'd walk
Sometimes they said nothing
And sometimes they'd talk

No one lived near them
Normal kids weren't around
Their scary neighborhood
The dark side of town

Dreary's house was white
And all made of bone
The walls were all done
In rows of gravestone

Naughty's home was of red
And the windows of skin
The walls were of fire
The roof of hot tin

Dreary had parents
Who looked much like him
They were mostly skeletal
And terribly thin

Naughty she had
Both a mom and a dad
And though they were evil
They always looked glad

Despite their appearance
Both folks loved their kid
So when they got home
They'd ask what they did

Both of the friends
Told their parents of gym
And their resulting performance
Which often was dim

Dreary was fragile
Not much of a runner
When checked during rough play
It was often a bummer

When Dreary was injured
The other kids scoffed
The coach just looked down
And said "Walk it off"

By school regulation
Naughty was forced to play
So when she'd tend goal
She'd stop it her way

Once they were home
They'd talk on the phone
From up in their rooms
They were never alone

They'd chat and they'd speak
Long into the night
About how school was awful
How the kids weren't all right

They'd contemplate ways
To both stay home sick
And thought up excuses
Their parents would pick

Dreary tried often
The fake sick routine
He'd point to his jawbone
Or his missing spleen

On the days that he'd try
To not go to school
It never did work
His mom was no fool

He'd plead for a bit
To try and stay in
His parents said no
With a white toothy grin

"Why can't I be home-schooled?
Why can't I learn here?
Why must I go
Where all the kids jeer?"

His dad said "Buck Up"
His mom gave him cheers
They sent him away
To learn with his "peers"

Naugthy tried also
To pass her fake ills
Instead of a fever
She'd complain of the chills

Her Dad soon caught on
She was being a liar
And filled her right up
With a shot full of fire

While Dreary and Naughty
Were forced to attend
The other kids opinions
They just could not bend

"These two, they are different
This pair they aren't cool"
Or so it was said
by the kids in the school

"The boy is a monster"
"The girl is one too"
"They both really scare us"
"Oh, what shall we do?"

They talked and they talked
Well into the night
About the odd pair
That gave off such fright

And so those mean kids
All hatched up a threat
They schemed and they whispered
To relieve their fret

When it was morning
Came the dawn with a plan
They'd finished their scheme
And so it began

And so the next day
When no one was looking
They captured the duo
And got their plan cooking

"The boy must be buried
The girl must be burned
They're just too darn weird
And so they are spurned"

"Get them, they're different"
"I think this one's dead!"
"That girl's got horns
Coming out of her head"

"They're just not like us
They sure don't fit in
We're all afraid
Of her confident grin"

They buried the boy
Who was made of bone
Alongside the girl
Who smelled of brimstone

So when school did end
And the pair didn't come home
The dark side of town
Was chilled to the bone

Dreary and Naughty
were nowhere to be found
No smart-ass remarks
No sad mellow sound

But those kids, they got theirs
The two were not dead
Their parents did miss them
And got angry instead

Calling on minions
Of fire and bone
They dug up their children
And brought them both home

The following events
All did make the news
As other kids' folks
Soon did sing the blues

The boys and the girls
All soon disappeared
Victims of parents
of those they most feared

Obituaries read
Were often quite gruesome
And echoed of themes
Of a fearful young twosome

So what can be learned?
What does resonate?
Which moral will stay
To make you feel great?

Don't ostracize those
Who are not like you
Accept them with kindness
Is what you should do

For one never knows
By the cover of the book
What lies underneath
So do take a look

What more can be said
To save you your breath...

Don't pick on the children
Of the Devil and Death

Deadicated to
the misunderstood, the
under-appreciated, the confused,
the troubled, the anxiety ridden,
the overlooked, and the
lonely everywhere

 Coming in 2004 - Friday the 13th of February